David - For Paula, Ryan & Leo. My love, my rock and my inspiration

Sue - For Ben who gave me courage

First published 2019 by MEBooks

46 Poppy Drive, Ampthil, Bedfordshire, MK45 2AW

This edition published 2019

The right of David Anderson to be identified as author and Sue Dooley to be identified as illustrator of this work has been asserted by them in accordance with the Copyright, Designs and Patents Act 1998

This book has been typeset in Brandon Grotesque

Printed in the United Kingdom • ISBN number 978-1-5272-4370-5

A catalogue record for this book is available from the British Library

www.pepthepoet.co.uk

introducing...

Peter Pants

& his Collection of Silly Poems

words by **David Anderson**   illustrated by **Sue Dooley**

Contents

Peter Pants

Peter Pants began to dance
around the bedroom floor.
The washing basket all looked on,
the clothes they yelled for more.

Fifi French, the flirty shirt,
whispered, "Pete I love your thing."
Vin the Vest was dead impressed
and he was completely made of string.

Peter spun, ducked and dived
and flew backwards in mid-air.
Ian Tie said, "I'll have some o' that!"
and slithered from the chair.

Jim and Jock, the tartan socks,
began to rock and roll.
But Jock the Sock said, "We'll have to stop…
Jim, we've got a hole."

The sponge and the flannel danced the 'Cha-cha-cha.'
The hand towel the Boogaloo.
Pete gave a wink to the lady in pink.
Saying, "Madam, how do you do?"

Pretty soon the party parted.
In walked a superstar.
She was white, she was lacy, she was rather racy.
Her name was Barbara Bra.

Barbara sauntered up to Peter
and grabbed him by his 'Y.'
She kissed his cheek, his knees went weak.
Then he began to cry.

"Oh Barbara my love,
'tis well beyond a joke.
I'm an old pair o' pants,
I don't want to dance.
An' I think me elastic's broke."

The Snail Murderer

Crack! I've just crushed a snail.

Do you think I'll go to jail?

I won't tell, if you don't tell.

I'm sure he'll get another shell.

You must think I'm an awful thug.

'Coz without his shell, he looks like a slug.

Johnny Conkers

My mate Johnny's really bonkers.

He spent all autumn eating conkers.

It's Christmas now an' he's in floods of tears.

'Coz he's got horse chestnuts, growin' out of his ears.

Brother Bashing Machine

I read about this man from Aberdeen.

He says he's invented a cool machine.

Apparently, it's like no other.

You can program it

to beat up your brother.

I say, "Fair play to you Mister,

now design one that'll thrash my sister!"

Terry the Tadpole

I'm Terry the Tadpole

and I live in a bog.

Mum says that when I'm older,

I'll look like a frog.

To be a frog

would be such an honour.

Because at the moment,

I look like a comma.

Get up! Get Up!

I'm in bed - I'm yawning.

It's 7.30 a.m. - in the morning.

Five minutes earlier - I was snoring.

Mum's downstairs - she's roaring.

"Get up! Get up! - It's your last warning."

The breakfast cereal - she's pouring.

All her threats - I'm just ignoring.

I'd rather be outside - exploring.

I hate school - it's boring.

It's 7.35 a.m. - in the morning.

I'm in bed – yes I'm yawning.

Ten minutes ago - I was snoring.

My Dad Can Fight Your Dad

My dad can fight your dad.

Mine's as hard as old nails.

He ain't scared o' nuffin',

not even snails.

He can fight dragons,

there was one in my room.

He was straight in there,

with a dustpan and broom.

He ain't scared o' spiders,

or anyfink creepy.

He protects me at night,

when I'm feeling sleepy.

He's as strong as the wind

and as big as a tree.

I love my Dad!

And my Dad loves me!

Similes 'n' Stuff

"Right!" she shouted as loud as a hawk.

"Detention for the next little worm that I hear talk."

She stood there proudly; like the devil herself.

She had a mouth like a goblin and the ears of an elf.

Her breath smelt like a thousand eggs.

She had a wandering eye and stick thin legs.

Her stare was as cold as a night in a freezer.

She had a big hooked nose like Julius Caesar.

Hair as dry as an old haystack.

A big pot belly and a hump on her back.

Hairy warts on her nose like a frayed reef knot.

A big round bottom that wobbled a lot.

This was my teacher when I was young.

I'm starting a campaign to get her hung.

I can hear her say, "Your grammar's all wrong."

"Oh shut up Miss! 'coz you really pong!"

Miss Has Won The Lottery

Since Miss has won the lottery,

things are just not the same.

She used to be grumpy and frumpy,

now she's incredibly vain.

There's mirrors all over our classroom

and her perfume fills the air.

She's stuck little diamonds around the edge

of her desk,

she has a throne instead of a chair!

We've all had solid gold fountain pens

that she bought whilst out in Milan.

They were delivered to school by Giuseppe,

a spotty youth in a green, rusty van.

She sits and files her nails at the desk

and we have to work on our own.

Her butler does all her marking,

whilst she sits and chats on the phone.

Our PE bags are made by Gucci.

Our uniforms: Christian Dior!

She's taken to talking in French all the time,

it's all this, "Merci", "Très bon" and "bonjour."

She gives out £20 notes for good work.

A smack around the head if you're bad.

I've heard she's got a job in L.A. next year.

To tell you the truth, I'm quite glad.

Yeah. Since Miss has won the lottery,

things are just not the same.

She used to be grumpy and frumpy

now she's incredibly vain.

Whingin' Ginger Ninja

I'm a whingin' ginger ninja.

This fighting makes no sense.

I'd rather be baking cupcakes,

than all of this self-defence.

I'm a whingin' ginger ninja.

I operate much by stealth.

Crawling about in the dark of night,

I'm making a right fool of myself.

I'm a whingin' ginger ninja.

I'm the king of martial art.

I'm forced to eat rice all the time,

I hate it!   And it makes me... ill.

Ant from Anfield

(To be recited in a Scouse accent)

Eh! Eh! You looking at me?

I'm as strong as an Ox, Lah.

The size of a pea.

Petit Pois.

That's French!

Look at me pecs,

I'm well hench.

When I'm older

an' leave the school,

I'll don the red

an' play for The Pool.

Yeah... Antfield!

That's where I'll play.

I can have you mate...

Any day!

Brummie Bumble Bee
(To be recited in a Brummie accent)

I'm a bee that's what I am.

The Bumble type,

from Birmingham.

I buzz around,

both near and far.

From Acocks Green to Perry Bar.

Down in Digbeth,

I dance a jig.

I'm not a wasp,

'coz I'm very big.

I'm No Lady

I'm no lady,

in fact I'm a thug!

Across the pond,

I'm a ladybug.

I find this all quite absurd,

when in fact I'm a ladybird.

The spots on my back

have a certain sheen.

Mum says I'm the scruffiest thing she's ever seen.

"We're a 'loveliness' of Ladybirds.

That's what we are ...

Remember girl and you'll go far!"

Earwig-Oh

(To be recited in a West Country accent)

I'm an earwig,

that's what I am.

People don't like me.

That makes me sad.

They say that I'm ugly,

all sorts of things.

They laugh at my pincers

an' me lack of wings.

I won't hurt you.

I'm not very big.

I won't go in your ear

an' I don't wear a wig.

Willie the Worm

(To be recited in a Scottish accent)

Am Willie the Worm.

I roll and wriggle.

Sometimes I cry,

sometimes I giggle.

I dig the dirt,

that's what I do.

Under the ground

an' away from you!

Away from birds,

that peck at ma brain.

When I pop my heed,

after it rains.

Fishermen grab me,

just for fun.

They stick big hooks,

in ma wiggly bum!

Being a worm

is a hard, hard life.

But I thank the Lord,

for ma wee wormy wife.

I'm a Spider Man!

*(To be recited in
a Geordie accent)*

Me webs are canny, just like me mum

Ah, the silk? That comes out me bum.

an' I haven't finished yet.

Av' spun al', neet,

Av' spun me webs wi' ma spinneret.

Av', spun me webs wi' Av',

think I'm gannin insane

Av' been spinning all neet an' I

above the frame.

Aye, up in th' corner,

Howay man, Am ower here!

and Wear,

from Tyne

Am an arachnid

Personify the Tie

"Oh my." sighed the tie,

suspended from the collar white.

"Alone am I, no friends have I,

to sit and chat with through the night."

Then a voice came, from beneath,

'twas the yellow polka dot handkerchief.

"I wish I were you instead of me,

you're on full view for all to see."

"You are lofty like the rocket.

I am crumpled and stuffed in pocket.

You are bought as a forget-me-not,

I am cold, damp and full of SNOT!"

Where Y' Been – Wheely Bin?

"Where y' been, Wheely Bin?" said Cheeky Tim, with a pert grin.

"Where've I been?" frowned Wheely Bin.

"My dear boy Tim, I've been to the gym, that's where I've been!"

"Have you joined the gym to get thin?" smirked Cheeky Tim.

"Why, do you think I'm not thin?" quizzed Wheely Bin.

"Nah! I was just wonderin' why you went to the gym

'coz you're definitely thin," said Tim.

"If you must know, Tim! I went to the gym but there was no-one in!

except Mrs Flynn who, I may add, was drinking Pink Gin."

"Drinkin' pink gin at the gym, with Mrs Flynn, isn't that a sin?" enquired Tim.

"Well that's up to him!" grimaced Wheely Bin.

"Who's him?" asked Cheeky Tim.

"Jim! Jim 'Blinkin' Timms! That's who's him!" growled Wheely Bin.

"So was Jim in at the gym, drinking Pink Gin with Mrs Flynn when you were enquirin'?"

"That's what I've just said," roared Wheely Bin.

"Alright - Keep your wheels on!"

... Chuckled Tim.

The Toad and the Kangaroo

(With sincere apologies to Edward Lear)

The Toad and the Kangaroo flew into space

in identical sky-blue rockets.

They took some ham and stacks of jam,

stuffed up inside their pockets.

The Toad looked out the window in front

and thought it rather bizarre.

"Oh, look at it Roo, please look at it do...

I think I've spotted a star, a star.

Oh, Roo, I've spotted a star!"

Toad said, "Roo, what's up with you?

You are such an awful grouch.

Oh, pray tell me, for I long to know,

what do marsupials keep in their pouch?"

They orbited Earth for a week and a month

or was it a month and a week?

Then a trump did the toad,

which made his helmet explode.

His spacesuit sprang a leak, a leak,

"Oh, Roo I'm starting to leak."

"Oh, dear Roo, what can I do?

You can see I'm awfully distressed.

I'm in disarray, I'm floating away.

I'm here in my pants and vest, my vest.

My very old pants and vest."

Roo upon toad, some pity he showed

and grabbed the fumbling buffoon.

Web foot in paw, they flew out the door.

They danced by the light of the moon, the moon.

They danced by the light of the moon.

Snowman Rap

It's a yo to ma bro an' I wan-cha to know.
What it's like being a man made out'a snow.

I said, "Yo! Ho! Ho!"

I got four black buttons made out'a coal.
I got icicles hangin' off my inner soul.

I said, "Yo! Ho! Ho!"

The hurt I feel, nobody knows,
It's no fun having a carrot for a nose!

I said, "Yo! Ho! Ho!"

I got a girlfriend an' a long to squeeze her.
She's got a big round bottom an' she's as cold as a freezer.

I said, "Yo! Ho! Ho!"

I wanna be loved. I need to have a cuddle.
Nothing too warm 'cause then I'd be a puddle.

I said, "Yo! Ho! Ho!"

When the sun comes out, ma cheeks they glow man.

I'm a shrinking and a sinking, I'm a meltin' snowman.

I said, "Yo! Ho! Ho!"

I can't sleep at night ma dreams der bad.
I dream ma family's all melted an' that makes me sad.

I said, "Yo! Ho! Ho!"

I wake up in the morning, it's such a relief.
The other night I dreamt I was in... Tenerife!

I said, "Yo! Ho! Ho!"

So it's a yo to ma bro and it's time to go.
Next time give a smile, to the man made o' snow.

I said, "Yo! Ho! Ho!"

I hope to see him before it thaws.
He's the main man. He's SANTA CLAUS!!

He's the 'S' and the 'C' - He's SANTA CLAUS! Yo!

Scarecrow Rap

Oi... Grrrrrr... Shove off... Boo!
Scaring crows is what I do.
Wiggle your bum.
Straighten your hat.
Stretch your arms.
It's The Scarecrow Rap.

Outstanding in my field that's what I'm told.
No need for money. No need for gold.
I got straw for hands, no fingers or thumb.
A wooden pole, right up my ... Back!

Oi... Grrrrrr... Shove off... Boo!
Scaring crows is what I do.
Wiggle your bum.
Straighten your hat.
Stretch your arms.
It's The Scarecrow Rap.

I got patches on my clothes. Holes in my hat.
Tartan scarf an' a pink cravat.
My best friends are potato pickers.
I wear dungarees an' frilly ... gloves!

Oi... Grrrrrr... Shove off... Boo!
Scaring crows is what I do..
Wiggle your bum.
Straighten your hat.
Stretch your arms.
It's The Scarecrow Rap.

I'm filled with straw from head to toes.
Socks for ears an' a button nose.
On my coat, a silver star.
A big brown belt an' a ladies ... shirt!

Oi... Grrrrrr... Shove off... Boo!
Scaring crows is what I do.
Wiggle your bum.
Straighten your hat.
Stretch your arms.
It's The Scarecrow Rap.

I talk to the sheep, the horse an' cow.
The man with the tan an' the rusty plough.
The chickens rabbit, going, "Cock a doodle do."
I hate the pigs coz they're covered in... little hairs!

Oi... Grrrrrr... Shove off... Boo!
Scaring crows is what I do.
Wiggle your bum.
Straighten your hat.
Stretch your arms.
It's The Scarecrow Rap.

I said a hip hop, hippity hoo!
Scaring crows is what I do.
With a big bang boogie
An' a biggety boo!
You can be a scarecrow too.

(So shout ....)

Oi... Grrrrrr... Shove off... Boo!
Scaring crows is what I do.
Wiggle your bum.
Straighten your hat.
Stretch your arms.
It's The Scarecrow Rap.

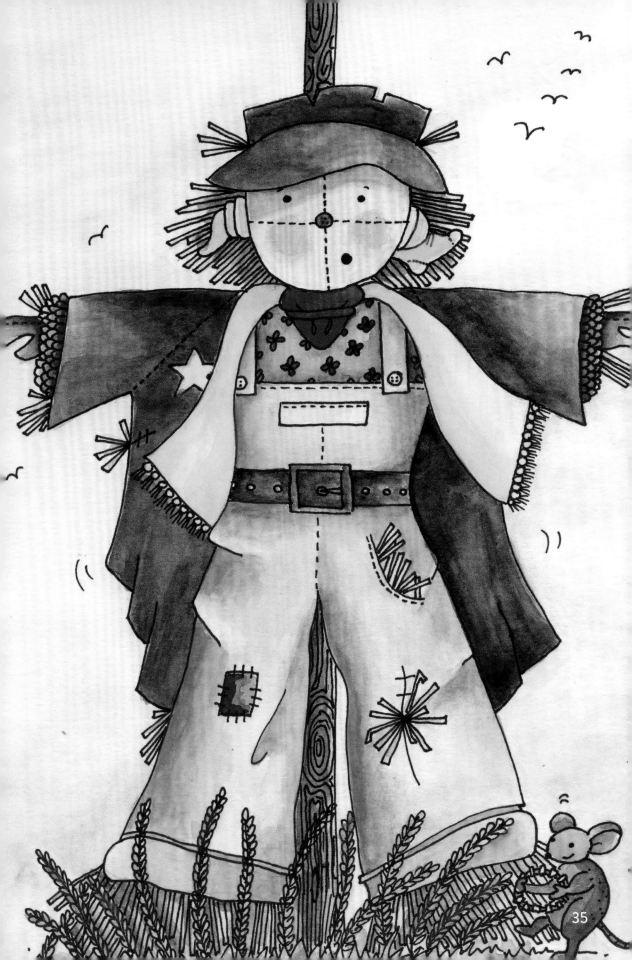

I Hate Girls and Sprouts.

I hate girls, worms and sprouts.

I hate my little brother

when he screams and shouts.

I hate bath times and bedtimes alike.

I hate it when the chain comes off my bike.

I hate Nan's kisses.

I hate being still.

I hate school dinners.

But I love being ill.

I hate my Dad when he watches the news.

I hate the words like: frock,

 vexed and snooze.

I hate being washed.

I hate being clean.

I hate strawberries.

But I love Ice-cream.

I hate my teaacher,

when ME she ignores.

My mum hates me,

when I'm slamming doors.

I hate pencils, pens, rulers and crayons.

I hate it on a Saturday - when it rains.

I hate the smell of cabbage,

I hate eating it too.

It looks disgusting and it tastes like poo!

I hate my sister, I think she stinks.

I hate it when spiders invade our sinks.

I hate it when old people

pat you on the head.

I hate getting up.

I hate going to bed!

I HATE this poem - so I'm gonna STOP!

Mattress Glue

I'm awake. I'm filled with dread.

Someone's glued me to the bed.

It happened when I couldn't fight.

In the darkest depths of night.

I must've known, I surely felt it.

The glue's so strong, I must've smelt it.

There must've been some cooperation?

For this clandestine operation.

A team of ninjas. It must've been.

In and out without being seen.

Stealth: their mighty secret weapon.

My sleeping cat they didn't step on.

'Ninjas R Us,' Elite recruits.

I bet my dog was in cahoots.

He growls, he barks, he berates me.

Since the vets, I know he hates me.

The alarm's gone into panic mode.

"Get up, get up, you lazy toad!"

I give it the meanest look.

He knows too well that I am stuck.

Being late just isn't good.

I'd get up if I could.

They won't believe my story's true.

As no one believes in mattress glue!